I Spy Colours

Story by Viki Bennett

and Nicki O'Brien

GIFT SHOP
FARM PARK ENTRANCE →
COTSWOLD KITCHEN

Litter

WE ARE
OPEN
Please Buy Your
Tickets
in the Kiosk
→

3

TICKET
ADMIT ONE

blue	
yellow	
red	(red mark)
brown	
green	

COTSWOLD FARM PARK RARE BREEDS

blue	(blue tractor drawing)
yellow	
red	(red mark)
brown	
green	

7

blue	
yellow	
red	
brown	
green	

9

blue	
yellow	
red	
brown	
green	

blue	
yellow	
red	
brown	
green	